## PRAISE FOR *APHASIA*

*A New York Times* 'New & Noteworthy' novel

'A rollercoaster of a run... [A] worthy journey and universal themes emerge... It's the 'as it's happening' narration style that makes Cárdenas's new work so innovative and exciting to read.'

*Chicago Review of Books*

'Long, breathless sentences dizzying and richly packed with memories, connections, and literary references. Cárdenas undercuts the idea of a single, stable identity and suggests the self as a many layered work in progress... Fans of the author's inventive, ambitious debut novel will find the same sardonic intelligence, paired here with a deep humanity... Original, richly felt, deftly written.'

*Kirkus* (starred review)

'Antonio, the hero of this manic comic novel, is a Colombian database analyst in California, worried that his sister's mental illness will upend his life.'

*New York Times*

'Brainy and decadent, playful and outrageous, *Aphasia* marks the comeback of the Self in a spiraling trip into contemporary manhood and the Latin American spirit that will render you speechless.'

Pola Oloixarac, author of *Dark Constellations*

'Mauro Javier Cárdenas has knocked down the novel as we know it, and built a cathedral out of the debris. *Aphasia* is monumental, funny, potent, and fresh. It marks a new beginning.'

Carlos Fonseca, author of *Natural History*

'Mauro Javier Cárdenas's *Aphasia* batters at the limits of guilt, of masculinity, of love and promiscuity, of the American family and English syntax.'     Nicole Krauss, author of *Forest Dark*

'In the follow-up to his wildly ambitious debut novel, *The Revolutionaries Try Again* (2016), Cárdenas again deploys his sense of invention and irreverence, jettisoning conventional paragraph and dialogue breaks and embracing long-running sentences that delight in playful exasperation... This quirky, playfully difficult novel will appeal to fans of Latin American fiction that navigates the bleeding edge of experimentation.'     *Booklist*

'Thrilling... A writer of originality who makes the English language sound like music.'

*Bookworm* (KCRW)

'Excellent... [*Aphasia*] dramatizes our growing ability to occupy multiple narratives at once — and proves that literature itself can do the same.'

*High Country News*